The Motorbi

One, two, three...Go!

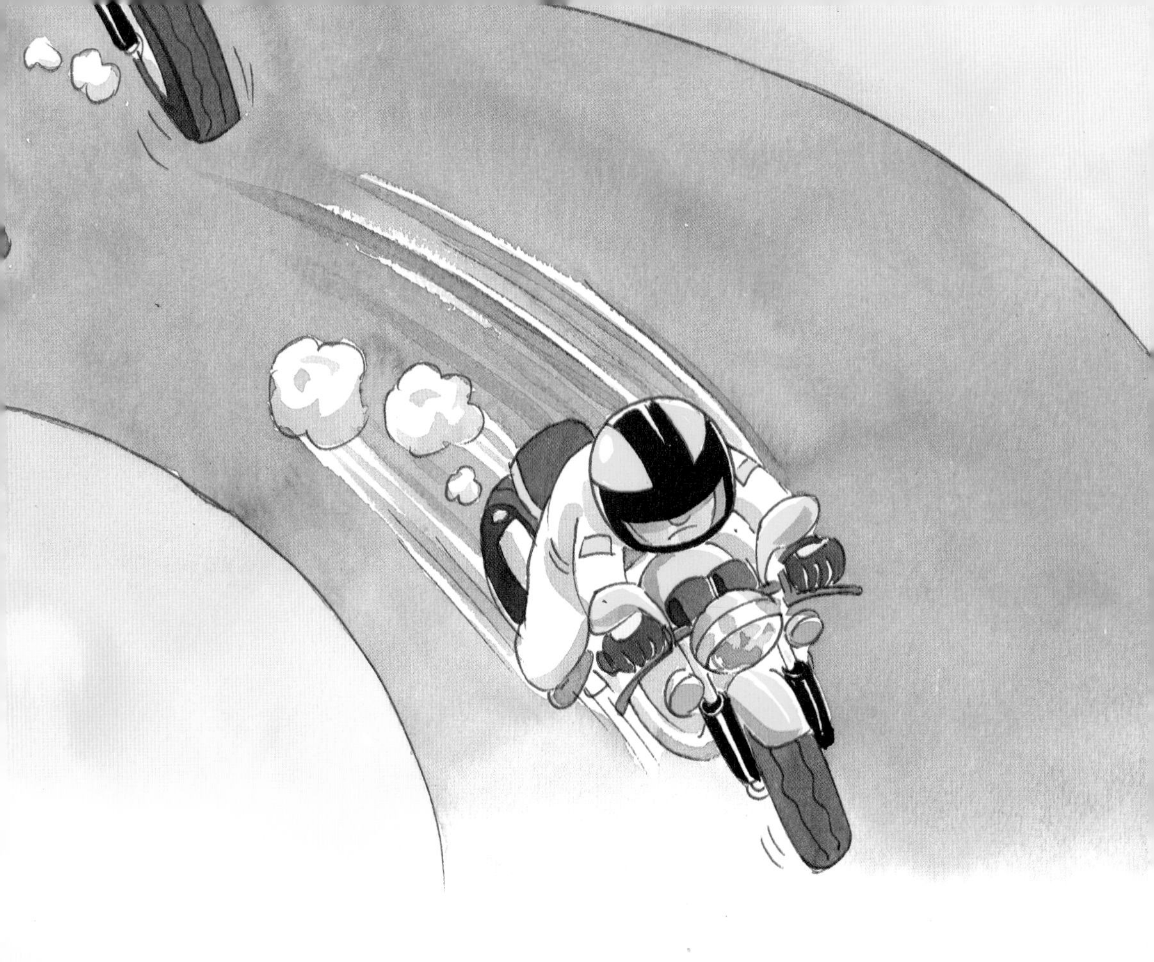

Here comes the yellow bike.

Here comes the blue bike.

The yellow bike and
the blue bike go very fast.

Look! Here comes
the red bike!

It is faster than the yellow bike.
It is faster than the blue bike.

The red bike wins!